Favourite Stories

In this series:

This edition copyright © Robert Frederick Ltd.
Downwood, Claverton Down Road, Bath BA2 6DT

First published 1993

Acknowledgements:
Typesetting by Creative Design & Typesetting
Illustrations by Frank Adams
Printed in Singapore

Jack & Jill

Jack and Jill went up the hill
    To fetch a pail of water;
Jack fell down
        and broke his crown,
    And Jill came tumbling after.

Then up Jack got and home did trot
As fast as he could caper;
Dame Gill did the job
to plaster his nob
With vinegar and brown paper.

Then Jill came in and she did grin
To see Jack's paper plaster.
Her mother whip'd her
across her knee
For laughing at Jack's disaster.

This made Jill pout and she ran out,
And Jack did quickly follow:
They rode dog Ball, Jill got a fall,
How Jack did laugh and holloa!

Dame Gill did grin
as she went in,

And Jill was plagued by Jack.
Will Goat came by and
made Jack cry,
And knocked him on his back.

Now Jill did laugh
       and Jack did cry,
But his tears did soon abate.
Then Jill did say
       that they should play
At see-saw across the gate.

They see-sawed high,
       they see-sawed low,
At length they both did tumble;
"We both are down
       we both must own,
Let neither of us grumble."

Then the next thing
            they made a swing,

But Jill set up a big cry,
For the swing gave way
       in the midst of the play,
And threw her into the pigstye.

The sow came by,

says Jack —"I'll try
If I can't ride this prancer!"
He jumped with a whack
on old Sow's back,
But she led him a droll dance, Sir!

Sow ran and squalled
           while Jack he bawled,
And Jill joined in the choir.
Dog Ball, being near,
           bit Sow by the ear,
And threw Jack in the mire.

Though Jack was not hurt,
        he was all over dirt,
I wish you had but seen him,
And Jill did jump
        with him to the pump,
And pumped on him to clean him.

Hearing the rout Dame Gill came out,
    With a horse-whip from the door;
She laid it on Jack and poor Jill's back,
    Until they both did roar.

Ball held Sow's ear and both in rear
    Rang against old Dame and hit her,
That she did fall o'er Sow and Ball,
    How Jack and Jill did twitter.

And now all three went in to see
To put the place to right-all;

Which done they sup,
           then drink a cup,
And wish you a good-night all.

THE END